Name:

How to use this book

The book is designed to use in one-to-one support of an individual or in small groups. The topics are very personal and it is essential that there is a high degree of trust between members of a group to gain the maximum benefit from the course.

The aim is to identify problems which people have arising from experiences in life. The solutions for these problems are found in the Bible. These solutions are applied through discussion, changes in thinking, action, prayer and the power of God.

The checkboxes are provided so that you can tick them when you have read and thought about the Bible passages. There are often a lot of Bible passages and you may decide to study some of these later when you are on your own. It is important to give time to reading the passages. Pray as you read. There is also a verse to learn in each unit.

The action stars are prompts for you to take some course of action.

Tick the big checkbox at the end of each topic when you feel that you have completed the study and applied it to your life as far as possible at the moment.

There are 10 topics each on a double page spread. You may manage to cover some of these topics in a single session. You may, however, find it necessary to spend more time on topics which are particularly relevant to your own situation.

I have written this book using the New International Version of the Bible but you should be able to use any other version.

I hope that Baggage Checkout will be helpful in enabling you to move forward in your life with God.

John Robertshaw

"May the God of hope fill you with all joy and peace as you trust in him, so that you may overflow with hope by the power of the Holy Spirit." (Rom 15:13)

the past

identifying baggage

your own timeline p22

☐

Draw a line with the years of your life (and dates if this is easier). Divide it into sections and write something in each section to describe it. Put stars on the positive and negative sides for events or situations which were positive or negative for you. Write something by each star.

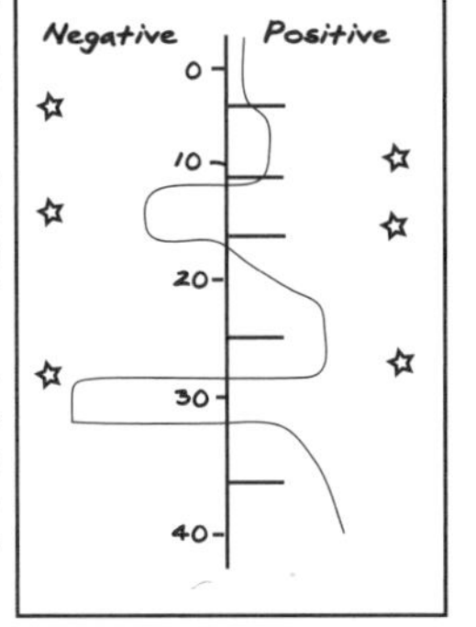

Draw a mood line which shows how you were feeling at various times in your life.

Talk about your timeline and identify any issues which you would like to address in this course.

We are all influenced by the past events in our lives. Some have had very peaceful and stable lives, others have had a very stormy time. Difficulties may have arisen from our own actions, the actions of others or they may be nobody's fault - just the expected ups and downs of life.

The aim of this unit is to review our past life, to face up to events, situations and circumstances which may still influence our lives and to consider how to deal with these issues.

If you have little baggage, you are very fortunate! You may, however, find this useful in helping others.

examples of negative life experiences

Parental Problems

- Poor relationships with parents or guardians
- Poor parenting - lack of care
- Adoption, fostering etc
- Parents were violent, argued a lot - alcohol, drugs etc
- Parents were unloving, disapproving, unpleasable, too busy, often comparing with brothers or sisters, conditional love
- Parent constantly ill or away frequently - death of parent
- Parents separated or divorced
- Parent bankrupt, in prison etc

Negative Experiences

- Conflict with family, friends, teachers - rebellious
- Bullying or bullied — name calling
- Failure in school, jobs etc
- Locked in a room or cupboard, fell in water, bitten by an animal etc
- Involved in an accident, seeing an accident, war, fighting, violence
- Loss of job, unemployment, bankruptcy
- Criminal activity, imprisonment, court appearances
- Serious illness, hospitalisation, disability
- Poor relationships with others
- Conflict with authority
- Bad sexual experiences, abuse, rape, homosexual relationships
- Abortion, giving up a child for adoption, unable to see children
- Serious illness or injury due to accident. Physical handicap
- Moving house, leaving friends
- Rejection by the opposite sex
- Broken relationships, separation, divorce, unfaithfulness in marriage
- Menopause
- Homeless
- Alcohol, drugs, addictions, compulsive behaviour
- Disappointment with someone you trusted
- Retirement
- Bereavement

Suggest some more

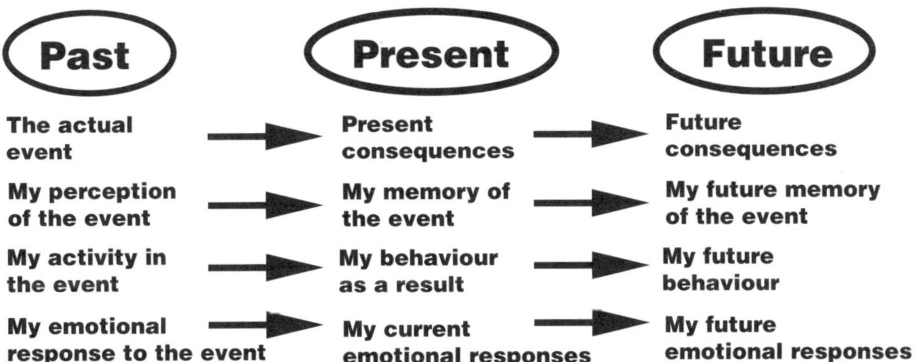

checkout

The past cannot be changed but God can help us respond to the past and enable us to live effectively in the future. Some key issues are:

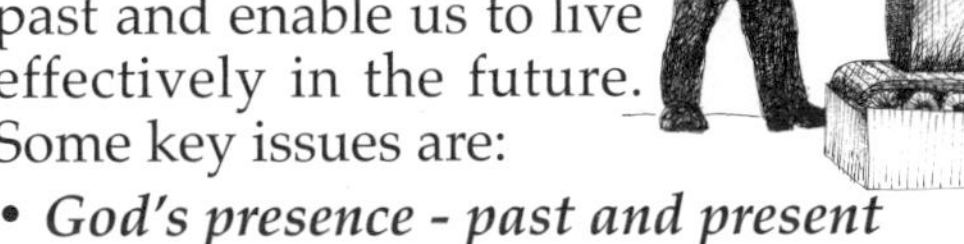

- *God's presence - past and present*
- *God's love for us*
- *God's knowledge of us from eternity*
- *God's purpose for our lives*
- *God's power and protection*

❑ Eph 1:4-5 ❑ Jer 1:5 ❑ 1 Pet 1:3-9

❑ Ps 139:1-16 ❑ Isaiah 46:3-4

❑ Read Footprints in the sand (p23)

We will look at four negative emotions and their solutions - here is a preview:

Guilt - repentance and the blood of Jesus ❑ Heb 10:19-22

Anger - forgiveness, love, prayer and blessing ❑ Luke 6:27-28

Sorrow - God's comfort and the man of sorrows ❑ Isaiah 53:3-4

Fear - faith and the presence of God ❑ Deut 31:8

inspecting baggage ❑

action!

This may best be done alone. You may find it helpful to write down your thoughts to clarify them.

- List any negative experiences which have affected your life.
- How do you remember the experience? What happened? How did you feel?
- What effect does the experience have on your present life? How does it affect your behaviour and emotional responses?
- Which of these feelings are associated with this experience - guilt, anger, sorrow, fear?
- Are there any things you would like to see change in the future?

confidentiality

Please remember that personal information shared in a group is confidential and should not be passed on to anyone else.

verse to learn

Therefore, if anyone is in Christ, he is a new creation; the old has gone, the new has come! 2 Cor 5:17 ❑

passage to read

❑ Ephesians 2:1-10

action!

be positive ❑

action!

Share about how you became a Christian and what God has done in your life

Yes!

I have read all the Bible passages and completed all the action points.

guilt

types of guilt

related words

remorse
fault
conscience
responsibility
blame
shame
disgrace
embarrassed
humiliated
indignity
dishonour
defame
unworthy
condemned

• *Actually Guilty*

We have done something which has broken a law of God or a law of the country or which has offended somebody else. We may or may not be aware of what we have done and it may or may not have been intentional. All of us are actually guilty before God (Rom 3:23)

• *Found Guilty*

Our deed has been exposed and pointed out to us and we have been accused of the offence and are declared guilty.

• *Feel Guilty*

We are aware that we have done wrong, broken a law, or offended someone. Conscience may be involved.

think

Think about events in your life for which you may be guilty. Were you actually guilty, found guilty and do you feel guilty?

❑ **action!**

human solutions

People use various techniques to deal with guilt.

• *Move the goal posts*

Change the standards of right and wrong and convince yourself that you were not actually in the wrong.

• *Find excuses*

Decide that there were good reasons why you behaved in a particular way. It is perceived as a problem, not a sin and it is not your fault.

• *Shift the blame*

Blame other people, the devil, circumstances or even God.

• *Cover up*

Hide evidence and lie about what happened.

• *Try to pay for it*

Do some act to try to pay for your sin.

conscience

Your conscience is your internal indicator of right and wrong. Unfortunately, because we are sinful people, it is not always reliable. Your conscience can be:

Clear - no feeling of guilt - but remember that God is the judge (1 Cor 4:4)

Good - in tune with the heart of God (1 Tim 1:5)

Seared - out of tune with God and his purposes (1 Tim 4:2)

Corrupted - the conscience no longer operates to protect against sin (Titus 1:15)

Weak - oversensitive conscience of immature or uninformed believer (1 Cor 8:7-13)

❑ ***Have you tried any of these solutions?***

❑ **Jer 2:22**

godly solution

1) Repentance and apology

❑ **Hos 5:15** ❑ **Mt 12:35-37** ❑ **2 Cor 7:10**

❑ **Ps 32** ❑ **Ps 51** ❑ **1 Jn 1:8-9** ❑ **Rom 2:4**

Guilt is good if it leads us to true repentance.

"I was wrong." Face up to your sin. Make no excuses or conditions. True repentance will include a determination not to repeat the error. You may need to apologise to God and to people you have hurt. Sometimes it helps to repent to God with someone else there.

guilty people in the bible

Look at each of the following people and consider how they dealt with their guilt:

- Adam and Eve (Gen 3:1-13)
- Joseph's brothers (Gen 42:21)
- David (2 Sam 11:1-12:23)
- Ezra etc. (Ezra 9:1-10:17)
- Zaccheus (Luke 19:1-10)
- Prodigal son (Luke 15:11-32)
- Adulteress (John 8:1-11)
- Sinful woman (Luke 7:36-50)
- Pilate (Matt 27:24)
- Judas (Matt 27:3-5)

❑

If you are in a group - act out one of these stories highlighting their response to guilt

action!

2) Restitution

❑ **Lev 5:17-6:7** ❑ **Num 5:5-8**

Do what you can to put things right. Restitution was expected alongside the guilt offering in the Old Testament.

why blood?

"without the shedding of blood there is no forgiveness"

Why does God require a sacrifice? When we forgive each other we do not demand a sacrifice!

The answer to this lies in the justice of God. If we go to a human court, we do not expect to be forgiven, even if we apologise - we need to pay the penalty for our misdeeds. This does not mean that the judge is unloving or unfair - it is justice.

God is the ultimate law-maker in the universe and when we sin against him we are found guilty in his court. We expect to pay the penalty.

The good news is that God in his mercy has himself paid the penalty for our sin through the death of Jesus. God has been both just and merciful. We can leave his court justified (made righteous) with a new verdict "not guilty" and a clear conscience.

❑ **Rom 3:9-31**
❑ **Rom 5:1-11**

3) Faith in the blood of Jesus

❑ **Is 6:7** ❑ **Heb 9:1-10:39** ❑ **Is 53:10**

The Old Testament sacrifices were only shadows of the true sacrifice of Jesus. As he died on the cross, he paid for our sin. As we put our trust in his blood, we can know the joy of sins forgiven, removal of guilt and a clear conscience. We are clean indeed! Only God can wash away sin.

❑ **2 Cor 5:21**

clear conscience

Jesus came to restore you. Bring your guilt to him, allow him to wash you and make a new start.

action!

verse to learn

Make every effort to be found spotless, blameless and at peace with him. 2 Peter 3:14

❑

Yes!

I have completed this study and know that my guilt is taken away.

anger

related words

anger
indignant
irritation
frustration
annoyance
displeasure
fury
wrath
bitterness
resentment
hurt
offence
upset
insult
affront
hate
jealousy
revenge

Anger can be because we have been "sinned against" or unjustly treated. We may also be jealous, proud or frustrated at not getting our own way. Anger can be directed against individuals, groups of people, organisations, systems, ourselves or God.

Testing your anger:

action!

- Is there someone you still resent for past influence in your life?
- Do you blame others for your present situation? "If only X had done, or not done this…then…"

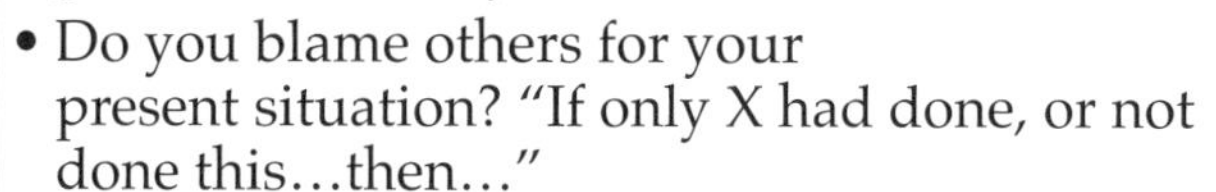

❑ *Apply these tests*

- Does the mention of the name of someone evoke a strong feeling of anger in you?
- Do you find yourself reacting to someone because they remind you of someone who has hurt you in the past?
- Is there someone you just cannot forgive?

love and forgive

action!

❑ Luke 6:27-36 ❑ Rom 12:17-21 ❑ Prov 24:17

Apply these solutions ❑

The words of Jesus are very challenging as he says what we should do for those who are our enemies, who hate us, curse us, ill-treat us, are violent to us or steal from us — in return we should love them, bless them, pray for them, take no revenge, and be generous and kind to them. So we will be sons of the Most High — be merciful, just as your father is merciful!

❑ Luke 17:3-4 ❑ Matt 18:21-35 ❑ Eph 4:32 ❑ Col 3:12-14

In our hearts we need to drop our grudges so that when we see the people again or hear about them we can be at peace and at ease. Also we need to be ready to verbally forgive should they offer an apology. It is often impossible to verbally forgive someone if they have not apologised since to do so may seem to accuse — but we can show love and lack of resentment by our actions and conversation.

advice on anger

- *God's advice to an angry man* ❑ Gen 4:6-7
- *It is dangerous* ❑ Prov 19:19 ❑ Prov 29:22
- *It is foolish* ❑ Prov 12:16 ❑ Prov 14:29
- *A work of the flesh* ❑ Gal 5:20
- *Get rid of anger* ❑ Eph. 4:31 ❑ Col. 3:8
- *Use gentle words* ❑ Prov 15:1
- *Don't fret* ❑ Ps 37:1-11
- *Resolve problems* ❑ Matt 5:22-26
- *Clear before night* ❑ Eph 4:26 ❑ Ps 4:4
- *Pray without* ❑ 1 Tim 2:8
- *Don't exasperate* ❑ Eph 6:4
- *Avoid angry people* ❑ Prov. 22:24
- *Be slow to anger* ❑ Prov 15:18, 16:32, 19:11 ❑ Titus 1:7 ❑ Jam 1:19-20

people in the bible with bad anger

Think about the motives for these people's anger

- Cain (Gen 4:2-6)
- Saul (1 Sam 20:31)
- Ahab (1 Kings 21:4)
- Asa (2 Chron 16:7-10)
- Uzziah (2 Chron 26:16-19)
- Haman (Esther 3:5)
- Nebuchadnezzar (Dan 3:13)
- Jonah (Jonah 4:4)
- Herod (Matt 2:16)
- High Priest (Acts 5:17)

people in the bible with righteous anger

- Moses (Ex 11:8; 32:19)
- Jonathan (1 Sam 20:34)
- David (2 Sam 12:5)
- Nehemiah (Neh 13:25)
- Jesus (Mk 3:5, John 2:12-16)

God's anger and wrath

In the Old Testament, God is described as gracious and compassionate and slow to anger (Ex 34:5-7). However, God's righteous anger is often provoked by:

- Injustice (Ex 22:22-24)
- Complaining (Num 11:1)
- Lack of trust (Ex 4:14)
- Disobedience (Num 32:11)
- Idolatry (Ex 32:7-10)

Judgment is often immediate. Repentance and returning to God avert his wrath (2 Chron 12:7).

In the New Testament, the wrath of God is averted by the work of Jesus. Although believers are rescued from his wrath (Rom 5:9), they still may experience his fatherly discipline (Heb 12:7-11, Rev 3:19). Unbelievers still fall under the wrath of God with its terrible consequences at the last day (Eph 2:3).

a story

❑ 1 Sam 25:1-44

Read this story. Discuss the anger of Nabal and David and the role of Abigail.

expressing anger

In the Bible, individuals freely express their anger and frustrations to God (Ps 56-59, Job 10:1-2, 23:2, Lam 3).

In doing so, they involve God in the problem, acknowledge that he is in control and that ultimately judgment lies with him.

righteous anger ❑

We may be rightly angry about some issue and of course this is not sinful. The problem is that righteous anger may lead us to a bad response and eventually into sinful thoughts and actions. (Eph 4:26).

Talk about any issues about which you have righteous anger. How can you prevent your attitude from becoming bad?

action!

verse to learn ❑

Everyone should be quick to listen, slow to speak and slow to become angry, for man's anger does not bring about the righteous life that God desires.

James 1:19-20

action!

Yes!

I have completed this study and am dealing with my anger.

sorrow

related words

distress
suffering
anguish
grief
misery
unhappiness
sadness
despondency
depression
despair
gloom
dejection
hopelessness
down
fed-up
loss
emptiness
disappointed
hurt
mourning

Some of our memories of events and situations may give us a very heavy heart. Sorrow is a perfectly natural emotion but it becomes harmful when it consumes, produces inactivity, is charged with self-pity, or when it leads to prolonged depression linked with guilt, anger or fear. Sorrow may be accompanied by tears, sighs, groans, being downcast, taking little interest in ourselves or others, sleeplessness etc.

Sorrow need not be self-centred. We may have a heavy heart because we have seen extreme suffering in others, great disappointment in the lives of those we know or other very sad situations. This may be connected with strong feelings, of love, compassion and sympathy.

loss

Bereavement is a most obvious source of grief but other losses in life can also give us a great sense of emptiness. Perhaps we remember happy days in the past which can now never be retrieved because someone, something, a situation or circumstances are no longer there. It could be loss of job, a house, a friend, a pet, divorce, retirement or loss of health and vitality.

action!

Do you have memories which fill you with sorrow? ❑

depression

Depression is a deep gloom and sorrowful mood that prevents one from functioning properly. For some people it can be very prolonged.

Look at these cases - See how they recovered.

❑ 1 Kings 19:1-21

Elijah becomes depressed after a wonderful victory at Carmel.

❑ Jonah 4:1-11

Jonah's misery is mixed with anger.

❑ Psalm 42:1-11

David is in deep depression and feels far away from God.

causes of sorrow

Find the causes of these sorrows:

Job	❑ Job 1:1-2:10	❑ Job 16:9-22
David	❑ Psalm 6	❑ Psalm 56
Hezekiah	❑ Isaiah 38:1-3	
Jeremiah	❑ Jeremiah 9:1-11	
A woman	❑ Luke 7:36-38	
A man	❑ Luke 18:18-23	
Peter	❑ Matt. 26:75	
Paul	❑ Romans 9:1-5	
	❑ Acts 20:32-38	❑ 2 Cor 2:4

comfort in sorrow

The God of comfort ❑ **2 Cor 1:3-7**

God's compassion ❑ **Lam 3:19-24**

God's promises ❑ **Psalm 119: 50, 52**

Our work for God ❑ **1 Cor 7:29-31**

The power of God ❑ **Isaiah 61:1-11**

The Holy Spirit ❑ **John 16:12-24**

The resurrection ❑ **1 Thess 4:13-18**

Future hope ❑ **Isaiah 35:10** ❑ **1 Peter 1:3-9** ❑ **Rev 21:1-4**

Support of others ❑ **Rom 12:15** ❑ **Proverbs 12:25, 15:30, 17:22**

Joy of the Lord ❑ **Hab 3:17-18** ❑ **Neh 8:9-12**

The Bible is full of sorrowful people who manage to continue to rejoice and trust God despite the troubles they are going through.

They are confident of the goodness and love of God and of his ultimate purposes for their lives. By faith, they see beyond the immediate problems to the great plan of God:

"He will wipe every tear from their eyes. There will be no more death or mourning or crying or pain, for the old order of things has passed away."

Jesus - the man of sorrows

❑ **Isaiah 53:3-4**

He was despised and rejected by men, a man of sorrows, and familiar with suffering. Like one from whom men hide their faces he was despised, and we esteemed him not. Surely he took up our infirmities and carried our sorrows, yet we considered him stricken by God, smitten by him, and afflicted.

❑ **John 11:33-38**

❑ **Luke 19:41**

❑ **John 12:27**

❑ **Mark 14:32-42**

❑ **Heb 5:7-8**

Jesus was a real man and displayed many human emotions - joy, anger, compassion...and sorrow. The fact that Jesus was sorrowful shows that there is a time and place for sorrow in our lives.

Isaiah describes the Messiah as a "man of sorrows" but also as the one who would carry our sorrows. As Jesus died on the cross, he accomplished a complete work carrying our sins, our sicknesses, our suffering and our sorrows.

There is comfort and healing for the sorrowful soul in the cross of Christ. This is the place to go when you are in sorrow and the place you will find the most profound help from the one who understands how you feel and can bear it with you and for you.

Apply these principles to your sorrow ❑

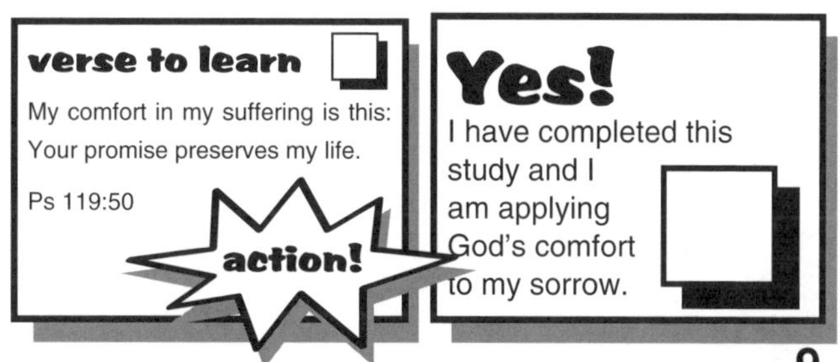

Fear is the natural way for us to react in dangerous and difficult situations. Sometimes we need to heed the fear and escape, at other times we need to face the situation with bravery and boldness. Fear, anxiety, worry and phobias become problems when they incapacitate us and prevent us from serving God and they can be linked with depression.

Fear may be rooted in the past. We may have had unpleasant experiences (eg abuse or bullying) which have made a strong fearful impression upon us - we are afraid of a similar thing occurring again. Or we may be afraid that something we have done in the past will be discovered and there is guilt.

related words

worry
dread
panic
apprehension
concern
anxiety
phobia
alarm
uncertain
trepidation
fretful
disturbed
disquiet
terror
troubled

fear of people

❑ Prov 29:25 ❑ 1 Sam 15:24

❑ Psalm 27:1

We should always do what we believe is the will of God and not give in to pressures and threats to do things that we are uneasy about. Remember that "the fear of man is a snare".

fear of death

❑ Heb 2:14-15 ❑ 1 Cor 15:54-57

Many people are afraid of death. For believers the sting of death has been removed and there is no need to be afraid. Death is a wonderful gateway to our eternal life.

phobias

Phobias are intense and irrational fears centred on particular objects or situations. Common phobias are fear of...

- Small spaces
- Large spaces
- Heights
- Crowds
- Dogs
- Snakes
- Insects
- Spiders
- Mice

Discuss any phobias you have - are they a problem? ❑

worry

When you worry, you think about an issue over and over again. You imagine all sorts of outcomes. You go to sleep thinking about it and wake up still thinking about it. You find it hard to relax or sleep.

People worry about all sorts of things:

- the future
- disaster
- health
- finance
- relationships
- failure
- being found out
- old age
- death
- confrontation
- career and jobs
- safety
- security

Worry can cause all sorts of health problems and can prevent you from getting on with life.

Jesus said "Don't worry".

❑ Mt 6:25-34

Are you a worrier? What things worry you most? ❑

do not be afraid

Many times in the Bible, God commands us not to be afraid - and for very good reasons:

God is with you	❑ Deut 31:6
God protects you	❑ Psalm 91:1-16
God loves you	❑ Isaiah 43:1-5
God provides	❑ 1 Kings 17:13-16
God is victorious	❑ 2 Chron 32:7-8
The peace of God	❑ John 14:27
The Holy Spirit	❑ 2 Tim 1:6-7
Seek the Lord	❑ Psalm 34:4
Pray	❑ Phil 4:6-7
God is our refuge	❑ Psalm 46:1-3
Our walk with God	❑ 1 Peter 3:14-15
Encouragement	❑ Prov 12:25

fear not...

God tells us hundreds of times in the Bible not to be afraid. He asks us to trust him, his love, his power and his protection.

Trust in God and his purposes for our lives is an effective antidote to fear and the way that we can live our lives to the full in the power and blessing of God.

... I am with you

Many times when people are afraid, God encourages them with an assurance of his presence "I am with you", "I will never leave you or forsake you".

Cultivate your awareness of the presence of God in your life moment by moment. If you know his presence, you will not be afraid!

As Jesus ascended into heaven, he left his disciples with these words:

"And surely I am with you always, to the very end of the age."

fear God?

This does not mean that we should always be scared of God.

Fear of the Lord is awe, reverence, worship and a realisation that he is the great creator of the universe and the judge of all mankind.

As with a good human father it is possible to respect, honour and obey and also at the same time to be a good friend with a close relationship.

Fear of the Lord is linked with humility.

Be zealous for the fear of the Lord. (Prov 23:17)

the fear of the Lord

The only fear which is recommended is the "fear of the Lord".

The fear of the Lord...

...is the beginning of wisdom	❑ Prov 9:10
...adds length to life	❑ Prov 10:27
...is a fountain of life	❑ Prov 14:27
...helps us avoid evil	❑ Prov 16:6
...leads to life	❑ Prov 19:23
...brings wealth and honour	❑ Prov 22:4

Apply these principles to fears which you have ❑

action!

verse to learn ❑

So do not fear, for I am with you; do not be dismayed, for I am your God. I will strengthen you and help you; I will uphold you with my righteous right hand.

Isaiah 41:10

action!

Yes!

I have completed this study and resolve not to be bound by fear.

baggage checkout 6

relationships

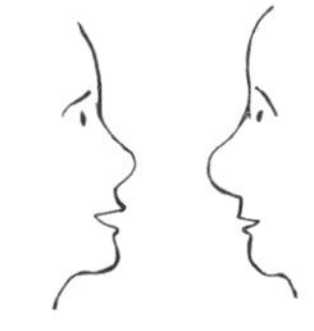

relating to parents

Our relationship with our parents is very powerful and formative as we grow up. Unfortunately there are no perfect earthly parents - some do the job quite well - others not so well.

Reflect on your own parents:

- *What were their strengths?*

  Be thankful for these!

- *What were their weaknesses?*

  Be forgiving for these!

action! ❑

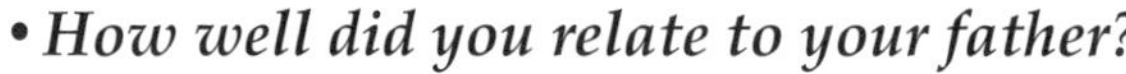

- *How well did you relate to your father?*
- *How well did you relate to your mother?*
- *What good memories do you have of your relationship with your parents?*

Some may find these questions difficult because of problems in childhood. If you are in a group, pray for each other.

Father God

Some people struggle to relate to God as their father because they did not relate well to their earthly father.

A good father:

- provides for his children
- communicates with his children
- instructs his children
- cares for his children
- protects his children
- spends time with his children
- gives gifts to his children
- encourages his children
- helps his children with problems and decisions
- is there in time of need

Do you have any problem relating to God because of difficulties with your earthly father?

❑

honouring parents

❑ Exodus 20:12 ❑ Exodus 21:17 ❑ Eph 6:1

- *How well have you honoured your parents? Are there things you could do to improve this?*

types of people

- Parents
- Grandparents
- Brothers and sisters
- Children
- Other relatives
- School/college friends
- Neighbours
- Friends
- People at work
- People at church
- Those in authority over us
- Those over whom we have authority

relating to others

❑ Heb 12:14-15

- Are there some people you have found it particularly easy or difficult to relate to?
- Are there some things you need to put right?
- Are there some ways you can improve your relationships?

action! ❑

how well do you relate?

- Are there some aspects of your personality which make it difficult for you to relate?
- How good are you at making friends?
- Have you had a lot of difficult or broken friendships - if so, can you identify a common reason?

relational problems

- Shy
- Brash
- Don't listen
- Talk too much
- Too serious
- Too frivolous
- Threatening
- Impatient
- Dogmatic
- Critical
- Gossip
- Over-sensitive
- Rude
- Bad language
- Moody
- Self-centred
- Nosy
- Argumentative
- Dishonest

sexual partners

❑ 1 Cor 6:12-20

For Christians, heterosexual marriage is the only appropriate setting for sex. Other situations are sexual immorality.

Sexual relationships with others (even a prostitute) makes us "one flesh" with them.

Many have found it helpful to take the following steps to deal with past sexual encounters:

- Repent of sexual immorality in your life. If necessary, repent of particular occasions you can remember.
- Pray and break ties of "one flesh" caused by your relationships.

marriage

❑ Gen 2:18-24 ❑ Matt 19:5-6 ❑ Prov 5:15-20

❑ 1 Cor 7:1-7 ❑ Eph 5:22-33

Your closest relationship should be with your husband or wife. The two become one and you are one flesh. Assess your marriage using the following scales:

	v good	good	med	poor	v poor
communication	❑	❑	❑	❑	❑
care for each other	❑	❑	❑	❑	❑
intimacy	❑	❑	❑	❑	❑
apology & forgiveness	❑	❑	❑	❑	❑
resolving conflicts	❑	❑	❑	❑	❑
working together	❑	❑	❑	❑	❑
faithfulness	❑	❑	❑	❑	❑
relating to God	❑	❑	❑	❑	❑

Your effectiveness for God may be affected by the condition of your marriage. Do what you can to ensure that it is in good shape. Are there steps **you** can take to improve your marriage?

❑ Col 3:1-17

Meditate on this passage and think about your relationships ❑

action!

verse to learn ❑

Therefore, as God's chosen people, holy and dearly loved, clothe yourselves with compassion, kindness, humility, gentleness and patience. Col 3:12

action!

Yes!

I have completed this study and am seeking to relate well to others. ❑

freedom

baggage checkout 7

sin list

These sins were listed 2000 years ago by Jesus and Paul - human nature does not change much!

- evil thoughts
- sexual immorality
- theft
- murder
- adultery
- greed
- malice
- deceit
- lewdness
- envy
- slander
- arrogance
- folly
- obscenity
- coarse joking
- impurity
- false testimony
- lying
- falsehood
- debauchery
- hatred
- discord
- jealousy
- fits of rage
- selfish ambition
- drunkenness
- orgies
- idolatry
- witchcraft
- lust
- gossip
- ruthlessness
- heartlessness

Mark 7:20-23
Rom 1:26-32
Gal 5:19-21
Eph 5:3-7

freedom from sin

❑ Rom 7:14-25 ❑ Luke 4:18

Our human nature is basically sinful and we can so easily slide into degrading shameful behaviour. Jesus came to free us from slavery to sin as well as from the penalty of sin.

Even as Christians, it is possible to get into a cycle of sinning and repenting and it is important for us to break this cycle if we are going to be effective for God.

❑ action!

taking stock

Honestly take stock of your life. Are there things that you continue to do wrong and don't seem to be able to master? Be determined to confront the issues. Pray and meditate on the verses below. Get help if necessary.

Jesus overcame	❑ Heb 2:18 ❑ Heb 4:15
The word of God	❑ Matt 4:1-11
Jesus sets us free	❑ John 8:34-36
Watch and pray	❑ Matt 6:13 ❑ Matt 26:41
Be dead to sin	❑ Rom 6:11-23
Live by the Spirit	❑ Rom 8:5-16 ❑ Gal 5:16-26
Clothed with Jesus	❑ Rom 13:14
God provides a way	❑ 1 Cor 10:12-13
Support each other	❑ Gal 6:1
Be equipped	❑ Eph 6:10-18

Think how to apply these principles ❑

out of control?

> Like a city whose walls are broken down is a man who lacks self-control. (Prov 25:28)
>
> ...for a man is a slave to whatever has mastered him. (2 Pet 2:19)

❏ 1 Peter 5:8 ❏ Titus 2:11-12

Our lives are battlegrounds and Satan uses every tactic to distract us from the work of the Kingdom of God. He will tempt us at every opportunity and preoccupy us with bad habits, obsessions and addiction. True freedom is being in control of our lives under the overall lordship of Christ.

❏ Titus 3:3-8 ❏ 1 Cor 9:24-27

action!

Do you have habits, addictions or obsessions which are out of control? ❏

Repent and pray that every part of your life will be brought under control.

addictions

Physiological or psychological dependence on a substance or activity which is damaging and which can only be broken with great difficulty.

- alcohol
- drugs
- smoking
- certain foods
- gambling
- eating disorders
- sexual habits
- viewing pornography
- exercise
- self harm

obsessions

Ideas or feelings that completely occupy the mind so that you can hardly think about anything else

- sport
- computing / internet
- games
- shopping
- eating
- slimming
- appearance / body
- a person
- money
- your home
- possessions
- TV programmes
- sex
- work
- safety
- superstition
- health
- religion
- politics
- cleaning
- washing

mental health

Mental health problems can arise for different reasons:

• Biological (hardware)

For some people, their brain is not working properly or damaged or there is some biochemical imbalance.

They need prayer for physical healing and medical help.

• Psychological (software)

For others, their thinking and emotions may have been disturbed by difficult experiences.

They need prayer, counselling and advice to help change their thinking. Medical help may also be beneficial.

• Spiritual (a bug in the system)

Some are severely afflicted by the devil or possessed by an evil spirit. This can affect both body and mind.

They need prayer and deliverance.

Some people have a mixture of these problems. Be careful that you don't jump to conclusions too quickly and seek advice. Jesus was particularly wise in knowing how to deal correctly with each case which came along.

family line

❏ 1 Peter 1:18-19

Some habits, attitudes, sins, obsessions and ways of living are handed down through families from generation to generation. You may want to pray to break these patterns in your life.

strongholds

❏ 2 Cor 10:3-5

Areas of our life which are out of control are like strongholds occupied by an enemy in our territory. Be determined to regain these areas for the Kingdom of God.

demons

If you think your problems are due to demons, seek help from those who can cast them out.

verse to learn ❏

Therefore, prepare your minds for action; be self-controlled; set your hope fully on the grace to be given you when Jesus Christ is revealed.

1 Peter 1:13

Yes!

I have completed this study and am determined to be free to serve Jesus.

the first three commandments

- I am YAHWEH your God...You shall have no other gods before me.
- You shall not make for yourself an idol in the form of anything in heaven above or on the earth beneath or in the waters below. You shall not bow down to them or worship them; for I, YAHWEH your God, am a jealous God...
- You shall not misuse the name of YAHWEH your God... (Ex 20:1-7)

most important

Jesus answered, "The most important command is this: 'Hear, O Israel, the Lord our God, the Lord is one. Love the Lord your God with all your heart and with all your soul and with all your mind and with all your strength.'" (Mark 12:28-30)

false gods

❑ Exodus 23:13

❑ Isaiah 44:6-26

❑ Isaiah 46:5-11

❑ Acts 17:16-34

Throughout history, people have been tempted to serve other gods, worship idols, participate in other religions and engage in occult practices. They would rather worship creation rather than the creator, bowing down to nature, the sun, moon and stars.

There are pagans, atheists who ignore God, and many who misuse the name of God.

Discuss your own past beliefs. ❑ **action!**

break

❑ 2 Chron 34:1-5 ❑ Acts 19:17-30

❑ Rev 21:8

Rid yourself of all false gods, idols and occult connections. Repent of any involvement.

Dispose of any charms, books etc which might be a snare. ❑ **action!**

forbidden occult practices

❑ Deut 18:9-13 ❑ Ezek 13:20

- **Magic, witchcraft, sorcery** - the use of supernatural powers, casting of spells, making curses
- **Divination** - foretelling the future and finding information by omens, signs, oracles and supernatural powers
- **Mediums, spiritism** - communicating with the dead
- **Charms** - superstitious belief in the supernatural power of objects worn etc

the true God

There is only one true God. He is the eternal God who made the heavens and the earth.

He is the God who revealed himself to Noah, Abraham, Isaac, Jacob, Moses, David, Solomon, Paul and others in the Bible.

His name in Hebrew is יהוה. The equivalent english letters are approximately YHWH and may be pronounced YaHWeH. (In English versions of the Bible, this is usually translated "the LORD").

He is one God but exists eternally as the Father, the Son and the Holy Spirit.

He is the God who revealed himself to human beings in the Lord Jesus Christ in order to save them and bring them close to himself.

He is the ultimate lawmaker and the final judge of all human beings.

There are no other true gods. All other gods with different names and different attributes are false gods. To worship them is sinful and idolatry.

idols in our hearts?

❑ **Ezekiel 14:1-6**

Idols are not necessarily physical objects. They are to do with our hearts - who or what is on the throne of our lives. Whom or what do we treasure most, whom do we serve, whom do we worship, and what are our priorities in life?

Establishing the rule of God in our hearts and over our lives is a defining decision for us.

Who or what is on the throne of your life? ❑

modern idols

* yourself
- sport
- pleasure
- happiness
- TV
- films
- holidays
- family
- house/home
- hobbies
- appearance
- education
- computing
- books
- magazines
- socialising
- drinking
- friends
- health/fitness
- cars
- boats
- gadgets
- work
- music
- pop idols
- personalities
- science
- arts
- sex

For great is Yahweh and most worthy of praise, he is to be feared above all gods.

For all the gods of the nations are idols, but Yahweh made the heavens. (Ps 96:4-5)

Therefore, my friends, flee from idolatry. (1 Cor 10:14)

Dear children, keep yourselves from idols. (1 John 5:21)

worldliness

❑ **1 Kings 11:4** ❑ **2 Cor 6:14-18**

❑ **Ephesians 5:5** ❑ **Colossians 3:5**

It is very easy to get taken up with the things of the world and to direct our attention away from serving God. We can become absorbed with materialism, work, activities, relationships and the quest for pleasure and happiness. It is then that we become vulnerable to serve other gods. Satan tried to tempt Jesus in this way. ❑ **Matt 4:8-10**.

Jesus said that although we may be *in the world,* we are *not of the world*. Our task is to be a light to the world - not to be extinguished by the world!

❑ **John 17:13-16** ❑ **Matt. 5:14**

❑ **2 Pet 1:4** *Are you a worldly person?*

action! ❑

happiness

❑ **Matt 6:33**

The world around us is looking for happiness. Jesus encouraged us to seek first his kingdom and his righteousness.

The path of obedience is the route to true joy in this life and to pleasures for evermore!

❑ **Ps 16:11**

verse to learn ❑

Be careful, or you will be enticed to turn away and worship other gods and bow down to them.

Deut. 11:16

action!

Yes!

I have completed this study and am putting God on the throne of my life.

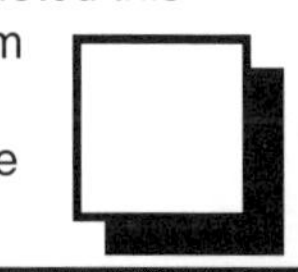

self image

❑ Romans 12:3

All of us have great interest in ourselves. We have a view of ourselves which may be quite different from the person which other people see. We have private lives, secret thoughts, life experiences and memories which are hidden from others but included in our own self image.

Some have a negative view of themselves and feel inferior, insignificant, insecure, or unloved. Others have an inflated view of themselves and are arrogant, believing themselves to be better and more important than others. The Bible encourages us to have a realistic view of ourselves.

self interest

❑ Philippians 2:3-8 ❑ James 3:13-16

It is also possible to be very absorbed with ourselves and our own lives. Jesus promoted and demonstrated a way of life which put the interests of others before his own.

How do you feel about yourself? ❑

action!

• pride	• jealousy	Are these good or bad?
• selfishness	• self-conscious	Do any apply to you? ❑
• self-centred	• self-absorbed	
• self-respect	• ambition	
• humility	• greed	
• self-denial	• confidence	
• self-control	• self-effacing	
• self-pity	• shy	
• self-neglect	• vain	

action!

feeling inferior

• Body image

Good looks are greatly prized in our society and we are constantly being shown very good looking people in the media and in advertising. We may be disappointed with our bodies and feel that this is a disadvantage and reduces our value in the sight of others. We may be unhappy with our face, size, shape, complexion, sexual attractiveness and there may be problems due to illness or accident.

• Personality

Society also favours those with bright, intelligent, vivacious, humorous personalities who are the life and soul of the party. It is easy to feel of little value if you are a person with few of these qualities.

• Background and situation

We may feel inferior because of our race and culture or because we come from a poor or dysfunctional family. We may have little education or speak with an accent or bad grammar. We may feel that we are less important than rich and successful people who can make their mark in society.

Failure

We may be particularly sensitive to failure if our parents have rewarded us and given us extra value when we have been successful but responded negatively when we have failed. They may also have compared us with more successful brothers or sisters or friends. There is an inbuilt belief that our value, security and acceptance is related to success. The problem is that failure, in education, business, work, relationships, marriage etc can be devastating to one's confidence and feeling of worth — you fail to reach your own standards and become self-condemned.

• Experience

Humiliating experiences such as abuse, rape, imprisonment and rejection can leave us full of shame and unable to face the world. Sin and wickedness in your past may make you feel guilty and worthless.

personal worth

In order to feel worth, we need to know that we have value and that we are loved. Affirmation by other human beings is helpful but if this is our only source of significance and security, it can be easily lost and life becomes meaningless.

Knowing God's purpose for our lives and awareness of his love and concern gives us a permanent value and worth which extends beyond this life into eternity.

God made me in his image	❑ **Gen 1:26-27**
God knows all about me	❑ **Ps 139:1-24**
God values me	❑ **Matt 10:29-31**
God loves me	❑ **1 John 3:1**
God has chosen me	❑ **Eph 1:11**
God has a purpose for me	❑ **Phil 2:13**
God will look after me	❑ **Psalm 32:7**

inner strength

Security in God provided inner strength for Moses, Job, David, Paul and, of course, Jesus. Even though they did not always have the support of other people, their confidence was based in knowing the purpose and love of God.

equal value

To human beings, some people seem more important than others, because of wealth, ability, education, or influence in this world. God has a different scale of values. All human beings are of great value to him, made in his image. There are no second class citizens with God. You are of great worth to him.

our bodies

❑ **Rom 12:1**

❑ **1 Cor 6:19-20**

Our bodies are given to us to work here on earth for the Kingdom of God. They are temples of the Holy Spirit and part of the body of Christ.

As we are clear about this, we will be thankful for our bodies and do what we can to remain strong, fit, healthy, pure and holy, ready to do God's will.

We can also be confident that God will maintain and protect our bodies as long as he needs them.

action!

Where is your significance and security based? ❑

verse to learn ❑

And we know that in all things God works for the good of those who love him, who have been called according to his purpose.

Rom 8:28

action!

humility

Humility is an elusive virtue - if you know you have it, you have probably lost it!

Humility is not necessarily the same as meekness. It is possible to be strong and confident and yet at the same time be humble. Moses was the most humble man who has lived and who knew God face to face, yet he was bold before Pharaoh and the Israelites (Num 12:3-8).

Humility is putting God and others before ourselves and being a servant. We are encouraged to humble ourselves and avoid pride. (1 Peter 5:5-6, Prov 16:18)

We are not expected to dislike, hate or belittle ourselves - indeed Jesus said we should love our neighbour *as ourselves*! We should have a good view of ourselves because our security is in God.

rejection

Many people feel rejected and respond by rejecting others. The best cure for rejection is the awareness of your own personal worth.

Yes!

I have completed this study and am secure in the love of God.

identity

what we are - image of God

❑ Gen 1:26-27 ❑ Gen 3:1-24
❑ Col 3:10 ❑ 2 Cor 3:18
❑ Eph 4:24 ❑ Rom 8:29
❑ 1 Cor 15:45-57

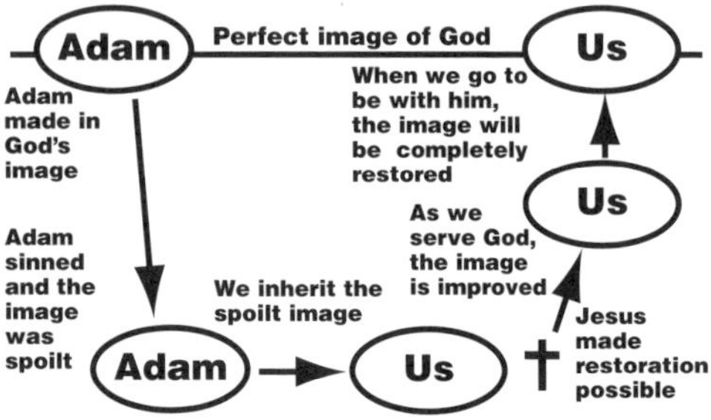

we are

- the image of God
- redeemed sinners
- believers in Jesus
- disciples of Jesus
- children of God
- temples of the Holy Spirit
- holy people (saints)
- God's elect
- the bride of Christ

Human beings were originally created in the image of God but this has been spoilt by sin and we all inherit a sinful nature. As we turn to God and serve him, the image of God becomes more recognisable. When he comes again we will be transformed to be like him.

❑ John 1:14 ❑ John 14:9 ❑ Col 1:15 ❑ Heb 1:3

Jesus was the only human being who was perfect, without sin, and reflected the image of God exactly.

who we are - personality

Our personality is the enduring set of our mental, emotional and behavioural patterns that make us unique and self aware.

Aspects of personality are not necessarily good or bad, but some may be more useful in different situations. We need to be at ease with our own personality and be aware that other people may be quite different from us. This will help us to understand them.

Consider the personalities of the following people from the Bible: Moses, Elijah, David, Peter, Paul. Think of others.

action! ❑

personality tests

There are many different personality tests but they all attempt to measure different factors of personality and then put these together to form a picture of the whole personality. The simple test on the opposite page is a five-factor test.

Most tests work by asking you a number of questions arranged in a random order. The results of these are analysed to give the measurements of each of the factors. No personality measurement is perfect, although the results can be helpful.

All the aspects of personality have advantages and disadvantages in different situations - for example in various jobs or roles in the church. You might think about which personality aspects would suit a policemen, a bus driver, a nurse, a scientist, a musician, a politician or other.

Simple Personality Test

Put a cross on the line at the point where you come between the extremes

Introvert Quiet, low key, deliberate, like your own company	———	**Extrovert** Enthusiastic, bubbly, energetic, like being with people
Disagreeable Truth and integrity more important than relationships, confrontational	———	**Agreeable** Friendly, value relationships, avoid conflict, interested in other people
Disorderly Disorganised, impulsive, unreliable, colourful, easily sidetracked, fun to be with	———	**Orderly** Prudent, plans, long range goals, avoid trouble, perfectionist, focussed, reliable
Relaxed Not easily upset, calm, emotionally stable, unflappable, secure	———	**Emotional** Intense reactions, easily frustrated, feel threatened, get depressed, moody
Closed Down to earth, prefer simple and obvious, well trodden paths, resistent to change	———	**Open** Creative, curious, individualistic, enjoy abstract, arts, science, symbols, change

action! ☐

Use the simple test above or do one of the many interactive tests on the internet. Discuss and compare your results with others. Do you think that your test results were realistic? What do others think? Does this help you to understand yourself?

the age to come

At the moment our personality is strongly linked to our physical bodies. In the age to come, it will be linked to new resurrection bodies. You may think of it as software transferred to a new type of hardware! (1 Cor 15:35-44)

how we are - character

good	bad
• honest	• rude
• reliable	• dishonest
• moral	• immoral
• honourable	• obscene
• upright	• coarse
• trustworthy	• impure
• respectable	• greedy
• polite	• selfish
• principled	• sensual
• decent	• foolish
• fair	• swearing
• just	• wicked
• patient	• conceited
• respectful	• prejudiced
• caring	• angry
• noble	• violent
• forgiving	• drunkard
• peaceful	• lustful

Ephesians 4:17-5:21

Superimposed on your personality is your character - whether you are a good or a bad person! Your character can change as you obey God and allow the Holy Spirit to move in your life.

action! ☐

Are you happy with who you are? Can you change how you are?

verse to learn ☐

I praise you because I am fearfully and wonderfully made; your works are wonderful, I know that full well.

Psalm 139:14

Yes!

I have completed this study and am content with who I am.

Negative

Positive

0

Now

Footprints

One night I dreamed I was walking along the beach with the Lord. Many scenes from my life flashed across the sky.

In each scene I noticed footprints in the sand. Sometimes there were two sets of footprints, other times there was one only.

This bothered me because I noticed that during the low periods of my life, when I was suffering from anguish, sorrow or defeat, I could see only one set of footprints, so I said to the Lord,

"You promised me Lord, that if I followed you, you would walk with me always. But I have noticed that during the most trying periods of my life there has only been one set of footprints in the sand. Why, when I needed you most, have you not been there for me?"

The Lord replied, "The years when you have seen only one set of footprints, my child, are when I carried you."

Mary Stevenson, 1936

Notes:

Notes: